W9-AXF-455

THE HUMANIZING OF
KNOWLEDGE

JAMES HARVEY ROBINSON

THE WORKERS' BOOKSHELF

In our modern industrial society, knowledge increases more rapidly than our understanding. The rapid accumulation of this unrelated knowledge greatly adds to the complexity and confusion of our life. As a result, the industrial worker finds it increasingly difficult to understand the world which he has done so much to create. The task of workers' education is to interpret modern industrial society to the worker that he may better understand his relationship to the industry in which he works and to the society in which he lives.

The Workers' Bookshelf has been conceived as a conscious attempt to meet this need for the workers for social understanding by a restatement of some of the fundamental problems of modern industrial society in simple language. The bookshelf has been designed primarily to satisfy the cultural aspirations of the men and women workers in industry. The books will not be limited either in the range of subjects or in number. Art, literature, natural sciences, as well as the social sciences, will be included. New titles will be added as the demand for them becomes apparent. In a strict sense these books may become text-books for use in the development of the movement for workers' education. In a larger sense they will become the nucleus of a library for workingmen. The fact that these titles are prepared for a particular group will not restrict their interest for the general reader, it will enhance it.

THE WORKERS' BOOKSHELF

In form and appearance, the Workers' Bookshelf presents certain distinctive features. Scholarship, a scientific attitude toward facts, and simplicity of style will prevail.

The books on the social sciences will be evolved from human experience. Each volume will begin as a class outline and will receive the suggestions and criticisms of the men and women who are the human factors in the industrial world. Each book will be adequately brief that it may present the subject clearly without becoming an exhaustive treatise. References will help the reader to more detailed sources, a large clear type-page will facilitate reading. Finally, the books will be bound in paper and sold at a price within the range of all.

The Workers' Bookshelf will contain no volumes on trade training nor books which give short cuts to material success. The reasons which will finally determine the selection of titles for the Workers' Bookshelf will be because they enrich life, because they illumine human experience, and because they deepen men's understanding.

EDITORIAL COMMITTEE

The Workers' Bookshelf

THE WORKERS' BOOKSHELF

Now Published:

THE HUMANIZING OF KNOWLEDGE
> *James Harvey Robinson*

Author of "The Mind in the Making," "Petrarch, The First Modern Scholar," "History of Western Europe," "The New History," etc.

THE CONTROL OF WAGES
> *Walton Hamilton*, PH. D.

Professor of Economics, Amherst College; Instructor, Amherst Classes for Workers.

> and *Stacy May*

Instructor in Economics, Brookwood, A Workers' College

WOMEN AND THE LABOR MOVEMENT
> *Alice Henry*

Editor "Life and Labor," Director of Training School for Women Workers in Industry.

JOINING IN PUBLIC DISCUSSION

A STUDY OF EFFECTIVE SPEECHMAKING FOR MEMBERS OF LABOR UNIONS, CONFERENCES, FORUMS, AND OTHER DISCUSSION GROUPS

> *Alfred Dwight Sheffield*

Associate Professor of Rhetoric in Wellesley College; Instructor in Public Discussion at Boston Trade Union College.

In Preparation:

THE POLICIES OF AMERICAN TRADE UNIONS
> *Leo Wolman*, PH. D.

Lecturer, New School for Social Research; Instructor, Workers' University, International Ladies' Garment Workers' Union.

COOPERATIVE MOVEMENT
> *James B. Warbasse*, M. D.

President of the Cooperative League of America, Author "Cooperative Democracy."

WORKERS' HEALTH
> *Emery R. Hayhurst*, PH. D., M. D.

Professor of Public Health and Sanitation, Ohio State University; Author of "Industrial Health Hazards and Occupational Diseases."

Published for

WORKERS' EDUCATION BUREAU OF AMERICA
476 WEST 24th STREET, NEW YORK, U. S. A.

THE HUMANIZING
OF KNOWLEDGE

BY

JAMES HARVEY ROBINSON
AUTHOR OF "THE MIND IN THE MAKING," "PETRACH, THE
FIRST MODERN SCHOLAR," "HISTORY OF WESTERN
EUROPE," "THE NEW HISTORY," ETC.

NEW YORK
GEORGE H. DORAN COMPANY

THE HUMANIZING OF KNOWLEDGE III

PRINTED IN THE UNITED STATES OF AMERICA

PREFACE

The active opposition that has recently been revived against those scientific discoveries and hypotheses commonly included under the general heading "Evolution" has led natural scientists to prick up their ears. When bills are introduced into state legislatures to forbid the teaching of "Darwinism," and biologists in conservative colleges are threatened with dismissal for holding the most commonplace views of organic development there is certainly need for renewing the age-long fight against traditional error.

This little book is the outgrowth of an address which the writer was asked to deliver before the American Association for the Advancement of Science at its semi-annual meeting in Salt Lake City in June, 1922.[1] He there urged that the task of reordering and restating the incredible accumulations of

---

[1] The address was printed in *Science,* Vol. lvi, July 28, 1922, and has been here incorporated with the kind permission of the editor.

scientific research so as really to affect public opinion sufficiently to discourage such reactionary enterprises as that to which Mr. Bryan has recently dedicated his oratorical genius, was an appropriate, indeed obligatory, one for the Association.

"An Association for the Advancement of Science," he suggested, "representing theoretical knowledge and some of its multiform practical applications, should not confine itself merely to forwarding the progress of research; coordinating, systematizing and applying the discoveries made. It must assume the further responsibility, in the juncture in which mankind now finds itself, of cultivating and spreading an appreciation of our best knowledge of man and his world among those now indifferent or actively hostile to it. We have every reason to dread unintelligence, but are as yet altogether too considerate of the unintelligent, for we know that they usually have the whip-hand. How shall we escape from his unworthy bondage?

"I am aware that the new organization at Washington under the auspices of this association, Science Service, is already doing what it can to spread the knowledge of new discoveries and keep the public *au courant* of scientific advance. I know that the admirably edited periodicals, *Science* and *The Scientific Monthly,* are performing the same service for those sufficiently prepared to read them with interest and understanding. But excellent as is this beginning we must make ready to go much farther by making scientific knowledge in its broadest sense an integral part of education from beginning to end."

The first step was to state the case, and furnish some opportunity and encouragement for those suited by temperament and training for taking part in the enterprise to coalesce. Among those who showed immediate active interest were Dr. Daniel MacDougal of the Tucson and Carmel research institutes, Mrs. Mary Austin, Dr. Edwin Slosson of the Science Service, Dr. Cattell, editor of *Science* and the *Scientific Monthly,* and Dr. William E. Ritter of the La Jolla marine laboratory.

Dr. MacDougal proposed that the matter be taken up at the Boston meeting of the Association during the Christmas holidays in 1922 and a session was accordingly held on

The Humanizing of Knowledge. Interesting addresses were made by Professor George
H. Mead of Chicago,[1] Dr. Sarton of Cam-
bridge, editor of *Isis,* Professor Lynn Thorndike of Western Reserve University, author
of *A History of Magic and Experimental
Science,*[2] and by Mrs. Mary Austin.

It will be apparent from what has been
said that there is a growing interest among
scientifically minded persons in the problem
of effectively disseminating scientific knowledge and a conviction that our efforts in this
matter have hitherto proved disappointing.
After many years of teaching and many hours
of conference with those able and disposed to
discuss the matter, certain fundamental conclusions have emerged which I am setting
down in the following pages. These conclusions seem to me to explain at once the failures of the past and to point the way to better
results in the future. In our efforts to teach
science and to popularize it we have over-

---

[1] "Scientific Method and the Moral Sciences," printed in *The
International Journal of Ethics,* Vol. xxxiii, No. 3, April, 1923.

[2] Professor Thorndike's paper, "The Historical Background
of Modern Science," appeared in *The Scientific Monthly,* Vol.
xvi, No. 5, May, 1923.

looked considerations of a very fundamental nature. It is easy to see why they were overlooked, but they must be included in our reckoning before any very hopeful advance is possible.

New York City.   J. H. R.

CONTENTS

I: On Mankind's General Indifference to Scientific Truth

I: On Mankind's General Indifference to Scientific Truth

Any most familiar object will suddenly turn strange when we look it straight in the face. As we repeat some common word, or regard keenly the features of an intimate friend they are no longer what we took them to be. Were it not for our almost unlimited capacity for taking things for granted we should realize that we are encompassed with countless mysteries, which might oppress our hearts beyond endurance did not custom and incuriosity veil the depths of our careless ignorance.

That I am "I" to myself and "you" to all my readers, who are each of them "I" to himself is on contemplation a perturbing circumstance. That the printed characters on this page should stir ideas in you is no easy matter to explain, and no one has yet been able to tell us why we and the earth so inerrantly attract one another. Yet these can hardly be called mysteries to most of us; so inured are we to personality, writing and weight that they are scarcely observed commonplaces.

Those to whom a commonplace appears to be extra-ordinary are very rare, but they are very precious, since they, and they alone, have built up our minds. It is they who through hundreds of thousands of years have gradually enriched human thought and widened the gap that separates man from his animal relations. Without them the mind as we know it would never have come into existence. They are the creators of human intelligence. The mass of mankind must perforce wait for some specially wide-eyed individual to point out to them what they have hitherto accepted as a matter of routine or failed altogether to notice.

These mind-makers are the questioners and seers. We classify them roughly as poets, religious leaders, moralists, story-tellers, philosophers, theologians, artists, scientists, inventors. They all are discoverers and pointers-out. What eludes the attention of others catches theirs. They form the noble band of wonderers. Commonly unnoticed things excite a strange and compelling curiosity in them, and each new question sets them on a fresh quest. They see where others are blind, they hear where others are deaf. They point out profundities, complexities, simplicities, involutions, analogies, differences and dependencies where everything had seemed as plain as a pike staff.

In short, poets, philosophers, religious geniuses, artists and scientists are all rare variants of the human species, who emerge here and there through the ages. Sometimes they make a wide appeal to their fellow men; often they stir their resentment or horror; most frequently they suffer neglect and contempt. A discovery to which no one listens is obviously of little or no importance. It is a mere private gratification which concerns only the discoverer himself. So the great question arises as to what determines the *success* of a new idea; what establishes its currency and gives it a social significance by securing its victory over ignorance and indifference or over older rival and conflicting beliefs?

To be received by the multitude of non-discoverers an idea must obviously be *acceptable* to them in some way or other. And what are the kinds of acceptability which promote the wide dissemination and the firm and prolonged tenure of beliefs? This is one of the most fundamental of all questions involved in human progress and at the same time one of the most difficult to answer. Indeed I scarcely think that anyone is in a position as yet to answer it.

For one thing, our acceptance or rejection of an idea or new bit of knowledge depends on unconscious and subterranean situations which are still very ill-understood. These are not amenable to logic as commonly understood, but have a mysterious, pigheaded logic of their own.

There is also a heavily personal element in belief. "Truth," as Lowell ingeniously puts it, "is said to lie at the bottom of a well for the very reason, perhaps, that whoever looks down in search of her sees only his own image at the bottom, and is persuaded not only that he has seen the goddess, but that she is far better-looking than he had imagined." Lecky, in his justly famous *History of Ration-*

alism, written toward sixty years ago, was in no position to reckon with even such knowledge as we now have of the so-called Unconscious. But he reached the true conclusion that in the general alterations of opinions, "definite arguments are the symptoms and pretexts, but seldom the causes of the change," and that "reasoning which in one age would make no impression whatever, in the next age is received with enthusiastic applause."[1]

Without going more deeply into this matter I think that we may safely assume that, in order to gain currency, a new idea must seem "good,"[2] and mayhap noble, beautiful

---

[1] The reader interested in this highly important matter is referred to *The Psychology of Conviction, a Study of Beliefs and Attitudes,* by Joseph Jastrow, 1918; especially the first three chapters. The manner in which orators, politicians, exhorters and mob leaders instil at least temporary beliefs, is taken up from a modern standpoint in *The Behavior of Crowds,* by Everett Dean Martin. See, too, *Public Opinion* by Walter Lippmann.

[2] By "good" I mean merely satisfactory in its general setting or emotional framework. In this sense the belief in the anger of deceased ancestors or in devils and witches and hell are all good. And of course the same person may entertain notions utterly at war with one another from a logical standpoint. See the vivid appreciation of this in "Dissociation of Ideas" in *Decadence and other Essays,* by Remy de Gourmont, 1921.

and useful, and that it must fit in pretty well
with existing notions; or at least must not
threaten violently to dislocate the accepted
scheme of things. If it is ugly, wicked, dis-
couraging, humiliating or seriously disturbing to the received plan of life it is likely to
be shown the door. Ideas like kisses go by
favor.

The *truth* of a new idea proposed for acceptance plays an altogether secondary rôle.
We rank the Good, True and Beautiful together, but it is shocking to observe how little
does the success of a new observation depend
upon its scientific or historical credentials.
In almost all we hear, read, say and come to
believe, truth, in the scientific sense of the
term, is a matter of almost complete indifference. It is irrelevant and may seem an
impudent intruder and marplot. We often
naïvely use the word "feel" for "believe."
And even the word "believe" has little to do
with evidence or proof but means to cling
to something dear and precious, and good in
our sight—to accept what we like to accept.
And the wonder grows that there ever appeared in this world of ours a group of men

so eccentric as to regard truth as the paramount issue.

If we make an exception of certain homely matters of fact which have underlain the development and practice of the industrial arts, mankind has until very recently been nurtured in the main on beliefs that were not submitted to any rigorous test of scientific or historical criticism, and which for the most part would not have been able to withstand careful scrutiny.   But it would be a grave mistake to assume that what from a modern scientific standpoint are myths, poetic fancies and gross misapprehensions have not played an essential part in the building up of the human mind.[1]

Man's beliefs had inevitably in the first instance to be what suited him and what he

---

[1] Charles S. Pierce, an austere logician, says: "Logicality in regard to practical matters is the most useful quality an animal can possess, and might, therefore, result from the action of natural selection; but outside of these it is probably of more advantage to the animal to have his mind filled with pleasing and encouraging visions, independently of their truth; and, thus, upon unpractical subjects, natural selection might occasion a fallacious tendency of thought." As Professor Jastrow, who quotes this (*Op. cit.* 39), adds, "Natural selection certainly has not interfered with the persistence of untrue and illogical beliefs."

naturally and easily grasped and clung to. For it is not the precise truth of an idea, as we have seen, that leads to its wide acceptance, but its appeal—its congeniality to a being with the nature and setting of man. There had to be a vast widening of the primitive imagination and vocabulary, and innumerable guesses about real and imaginary things, before a phenomenon so strange as modern science could emerge. Logical definition and speculation can operate quite as well—indeed better, on unreal presuppositions than on experimentally verifiable ones.

Among the wonderers and pointers-out the poet, who "fancy light from Fancy caught," whose "thought leapt out to wed with thought," has always been surest of a large audience. For songs, heroic tales and rhapsodies can be attuned to the heart's desire— they are magic carpets on which we can voyage whither we will. Their truth is the deepest truth—that of vague human longings.

When we are told that Kubla Khan a stately pleasure dome decreed, "where Alph the sacred river ran, through caverns measureless to man down to a sunless sea," we do not feel obliged to consult a list of Tartar rulers, or locate the sources of the river Alph, or consider the geological formation of limestone caverns. Few will be disturbed by the question of what particular species of wood louse secreted the honey dew, or the number of bacteria occurring per cubic centimeter in fresh milk of Paradise.

The truth of human fears, disappointments and aspirations is indeed the supreme truth, being made as we are, and is likely to remain so. All other truth, no matter how true, is in comparison dust and chaff, except for the few who owing to their highly exceptional temperament crave proofs and precision, at least in some narrow segment of life's circle.

Religion shares with poetry and romance the appeal to man's natural and deep longings and spontaneous inclinations. Indeed, among the many definitions of religion none is better perhaps than that of Santayana, to whom it seems to be poetry sometimes mistaking itself for science. Religion has concerned itself, at least during historic times, with those terrors, awes, obligations and aspirations which rest on a belief in supernatural beings, good and bad. It has to do with our vivid fears in a world of sad mischance; with the hopes, restraints and sacred duties which promise in some way to offset life's incalculable tragedies.

The poetic elements in religion are supplemented by more or less definitely formulated beliefs about man's origin and nature and the workings of the things about him. These convictions are commonly of ancient and untraceable genesis, although they may finally be very logically and precisely stated by a Thomas Aquinas or a Calvin and form a part of a closely woven philosophical system.

One may not, however, take the same liberties with religious beliefs that he may with the fancies of the poet. The adherents of a particular religious creed are not free to pick and choose, and to reject what comes to seem improbable. The "truth" once delivered stands, for it depends largely on the form of its original delivery. It is the word of the Most High or of some prophet inspired by him. At least this has seemed inevitable to a great majority of Christians and their leaders since the founding of their faith.

Religion therefore makes a double appeal, that of poetry and of divinely certified truth about all the great concerns of life.   It meets questions about our origin, duty and possible fates, without any call for painful critical thinking, suspension of judgment and dubious, ever-to-be-revised, theories and hypotheses.

II: The Dehumanizing of Science

II: The Dehumanizing of Science

These preliminary reflections have been necessary in order to introduce the scientist to us. He himself is quite as prone as others to take himself for granted and not realize what an altogether astonishing and even grotesque mystery he and his doings constitute. He, like the poets, philosophers, theologians and artists, belongs to the small and precious group of persistent wonderers. He is a questioner, a discoverer, a pointer-out. He, like them, gives meaning to things that would otherwise pass unnoticed.

But there is something inhuman in his methods and aims. He craves a meticulous precision of observation, measurement and statement quite alien to the other teachers of men. He exhibits an almost shocking insensibility to the cherished motives of belief. He does not ask whether what he looks for is right or wrong, beautiful or ugly, useful or futile, comforting or distressing. He only asks whether what he finds is an instance of something really happening. He persistently carries his analysis as far as he can and tries scrupulously to set down just what he has seen and the inferences he may make or suspect.

Moreover he interests himself in what appear to the overwhelming mass of mankind to be stupid trifles which promise neither pleasure nor profit. What difference can it possibly make whether a caterpillar has four muscles or four thousand, as described by the indefatigable Lyonnet; whether the light from metallic arcs may contain wave lengths as short as a six hundred thousandth of a millimeter; whether the solutions of the violet salt of chromium sulphate are stable at room temperature; whether there are a thousand or eighty thousand species of beetles. And in other fields, what does it profit a man to be able to point out the interpolations in the Book of Ecclesiastes, or discover the origin of the Edict of Milan or describe the marriage customs of the small and obscure tribe of the Todas.

And yet there can be no doubt that these and similar questions and their answers constitute the great bulk of scientific knowledge that has been accumulated during the past three centuries. This is stowed away in monographic contributions, proceedings and transactions under innumerable rubrics which no single man of science, no matter how broad his interests or how comprehensive his knowledge, could possibly recall.

This esoteric treasury of knowledge, the very existence of which is unknown, or indifferent, even to the so-called educated classes, is like a vast safety deposit vault with its many boxes large and small. The keys are in many hands, and few there be that can open more than two or three of the boxes.

Nevertheless the scientific investigator and the scholar has his own peculiar rewards. He finds a few like-minded persons to co-operate with him. Scientific research is not simply a solitary indulgence of infrequent and eccentric individuals. Little drops of knowledge coalesce into bigger drops, and odds and ends of detailed information gradually get shifted into patterns of great interest and beauty. For the world proves to be indefinitely investigable.

Then there is a flavor of high adventure in

the pursuit of knowledge. The investigator is to himself the hero in a romance; he is keener than the sleuth of the detective tale and knows it. He has his territorial disputes, his ententes and his wars with his fellow scientists.

It is apparent however that the sustained and arduous scientific research which has gradually built up our fund of knowledge is a pursuit for the few. It is far from a seductive occupation for even creative minds of the poetic and religious type. It often requires years to ascertain facts and record observations that will in the end fill a small, abstruse and technical pamphlet.

Research is mainly looking for things that are not there and attempting processes that will not occur. The layman has little notion of this. Experimental science is tireless fumbling and groping, or the laborious discrimination and comparison of detail. It is subject to innumerable disappointments in following trails that lead out into a boundless desert or up against barriers that it seems hopeless to try to scale. For the scientist does not make his own landscape, as do the poets, and even many philosophers, nor can he fly hither and thither at will, but he subjects himself to the tyranny of the natural phenomena or processes that he is observing. As Bacon says, he works "according to his stuff and is limited thereby."

The success of modern scientific emulation has lain very largely in its stubborn refusal to consider natural phenomena in terms of human impulse and mankind's native interests. During the Middle Ages the world was thought to be made for man. It was the vestibule to an eternal existence that awaited every human soul beyond the grave. As his transient sojourning place and scene of trial, it had a moral and edifying quality which underlay a great part of the speculation about natural things. Around about the earth were the heavens, the ever-perfect and incorruptible dwelling place of God and the angels, and of the blessed who were found worthy to see His face.

Those who began the reconstruction and further amplifying of knowledge, from the early seventeenth century onward, were on their guard against these older genial man-centered and earth-centered conceptions of Nature. The preferences of the observer were to be ruled out. He was to be merely a careful and neutral spectator who must not allow himself to become so warmly implicated in his discoveries as to sacrifice a whit of his eager indifference.

Of course this proud isolation was subject to many compromises, conscious and unconscious. And from a philosophical standpoint the onlooker, as has often been pointed out, is always one of the essential elements in the observing and recording. The ideal was, however, and still is, to *dehumanize* scientific investigation so far as may be. And this method has approved itself by its exceeding fruitfulness.

III: How Scientific Discoveries have Become a Matter of General Concern

III: How Scientific Discoveries have Become a Matter of General Concern

The question here arises, how did this scientific ambition ever come to be a matter of public concern? How did this professedly "idle curiosity," as Veblen ironically calls it, confined as it is to rare and eccentric intellects and affecting a superb indifference to human interests, ever come to influence the beliefs and daily lives of great masses of mankind?

The indubitable and ever-growing social significance of modern experimental science is the result chiefly of three historical tendencies:

1. In the first place, the minute and scrupulous observations and calculations and the careful inferences of the natural scientist have in a few cases formed themselves into such impressive generalizations as to catch the attention of laymen. Examples of such large reconstructions are the reduction of the heavenly bodies to physical and chemical

processes; a growing substitution of respect for so-called natural laws, and a corresponding decline of confidence in miracles and magic; the partial elimination of the diabolical in the theory and practice of medicine and the law; and, lately, the frank inclusion of man himself in the order of nature. This process of transforming a naturally unscientific creature into a scientific one has of course not gone very far, and the tendency has met with varied and insistent opposition with which we are all familiar.

2. In the second place, the inventor and engineer have in the interest of practical utility seized upon certain details of scientific discovery and, with the connivance of the business man, influenced by motives of pecuniary profit, succeeded in revolutionizing industry and inter-communication, thereby gravely altering the conditions, possibilities and problems of civilization. Scientific research originally carried on for its own sake has thus produced indirectly the most far-reaching effects on our daily life.

In the beginning, man was in no position fundamentally and permanently to modify his environment in his own interests. He had to make such terms as he could with the uncontrolled order of nature. To-day, through scientific knowledge and experiment he is constantly engaged in remaking the world to suit his convenience. He substitutes mechanical devices for the human hand; he generates and distributes new forms of power, and has even learned through synthetic chemistry to create an indefinite number of new substances.

Achievements of this class are the most spectacular outcome of applied knowledge and have done more than anything else to secure the scientist a specious popular esteem. But the problem is becoming acute whether that esteem is of such a character that it will permit the overwhelming process of readjustment to be guided and controlled by those best qualified by natural competence and training to prevent varied catastrophe.

3. A third less theatrical but none the less significant effect of the progress of natural science has been the influence which its ideals and methods, so successfully applied to the investigation of physical, chemical and bio-

logical processes, has had on the conception of man himself, his origin, history, habits and institutions. Anthropology, history in all its branches, philosophy, psychology, economics, and all other departments of research bearing on man's nature and conduct are undergoing changes of a momentous nature. So revolutionary are their implications that some recent writers go so far as to maintain that a great part of what has passed for the social sciences is obsolete; that it will fade away in the light of new scientific knowledge, even as the scholastic philosophy was supplanted by experimental science.

Man suddenly finds himself a bewildered actor in a new drama where he must learn his part all over again on pain of disastrous failure in his appointed rôle.

To summarize the preceding reflections: Modern scientific research, in spite of its professed aloofness and disregard of human feelings and motives, has succeded in unfolding to our gaze so new a world in its origin, development, workings and possibilities of control in the interests of human welfare, that practically all of the older poetic and religious ideas have to be fundamentally revised or reinterpreted.

Scientific knowledge, ingeniously applied and utilized by inventors and engineers has, with the assistance of business men and financiers, metamorphosed our environment and our relations with our fellow men.

Lastly, our notions of our own nature are being so altered that should we discreetly apply our increasing knowledge of the workings of the mind and the feelings, a far more successful technique might finally emerge for the regulation of the emotions than any that has hitherto been suggested. This is at least an exhilarating hope.

Now if all this be true we are forced to ask whether it is safe, since our life has come to be so profoundly affected by and dependent on scientific knowledge, to permit the great mass of mankind and their leaders and teachers to continue to operate on the basis of presuppositions and prejudices which owe their respectability and currency to their great age and uncritical character, and which fail to correspond with real things and actual operations as they are coming to be understood?

A great part of our beliefs about man's nature and the rightness or wrongness of his acts, date from a time when far less was known of the universe and far different were the conditions and problems of life from those of to-day.

Do we not urgently need a new type of wonderer and pointer-out, whose curiosity shall be excited by this strange and perturbing emergency in which we find ourselves, and who shall set himself to discover and indicate to his busy and timid fellow creatures a possible way out? Otherwise how is a race so indifferent and even hostile to scientific and historical knowledge of the preciser sort—so susceptible to beliefs that make other and more potent appeals than truth—to be reconciled to stronger drafts of medicinal information which their disease demands but their palates reject?

It is this paramount question that I have in mind in preparing this essay. I have not the space, nor indeed the capacity, to make its multiform and urgent necessity clear as I should wish. But many readers, I know, have already been thinking of the matter and will concede the necessity and urgency without further argument. Others will have experienced a vague anxiety and foreboding about the present state and prospects of scientific advance; and what has been said may help to clear their minds, even if they do not agree forthwith that the present crisis is of the precise nature and gravity that it seems to me to be.

Much has been written of the conflict of science and religion. But this is to narrow down the real problem, which is nothing less than the stupendous task of cultivating an appreciation of the nature and significance of precise thought and exact knowledge in a being by nature and nurture so careless of truth and so given to modes of thinking repugnant to scientific intelligence.

Even the more magnificent scientific discoveries, especially those of recent years, have not penetrated into our general education, and are entirely disregarded in most discussions of social problems. And yet an imposing accumulation of critical information of wide bearing is at our disposal which might become an active factor in the readjustment of the troubled relations of man were it possible to overcome the obstacles to its general dissemination and acceptance.

IV: Present Organized Opposition to the Scientific View of Man's Place in the Natural Order

IV: Present Organized Opposition to the Scientific View of Man's Place in the Natural Order

A striking illustration of the ineffectiveness of our present methods of popularizing cardinal scientific discoveries has recently been supplied by the revival of a strong and threatening opposition to the knowledge we now have of man's affinity and obvious relationships with the rest of the organic world.

The idea of evolution is perhaps the most momentous in its bearings of all the great generalizations which have come with increased knowledge of the history of our globe and of its inhabitants. Those who will take the trouble to consider even in the most elementary manner the multifold and concurrent evidence of the successive appearance of vegetable and animal species on the earth and the reasons for including man among the primates, can not fail, unless they be utterly blinded by prejudice, to concede our animal background, and welcome the light that this discovery sheds on human failures and possibilities.

The matter has been set forth by skillful writers such as Huxley, Wallace, Haeckel, John Fiske, Geddes, Drummond and others in a manner so plain and convincing that it would seem that no one would have the slightest inclination to take issue with them on the general proposition. But to judge from the conscious and unconscious confusion that seems to prevail in the minds of many, the matter is still very ill-understood by even intelligent laymen.

Recently a serious misunderstanding has resulted from the report that men of science are giving up "Darwinism"—that "Darwinism is dead." This has puzzled those who supposed that evolution was a well-substantiated assumption, and has filled with a somewhat malicious joy those who have always denounced the notion as wicked and opposed to Scripture.

To the public, Darwinism means evolution, man's monkey origin, as the matter is popu-

larly but inexactly phrased. But to the pale-
ontologist and biologist Darwinism does not
mean the theory of man's animal descent,
(which was formulated long before the publication of the *Origin of Species*). To them,
it means the ingenious theories which Darwin
so patiently worked out to account for *the
facts of evolution.* The statement that Darwinism is dead does not imply that the evidence for the evolutionary hypothesis has in
any way been weakened or that any really
competent man of science doubts our animal
derivation. It only means that Darwin's ex-
planations of how one species may have been
derived from another have proved, as a result
of increasing knowledge, to be mistaken or
inadequate. It means that we can not any
longer assign the importance he did to
sexual and natural selection and the hered-
itary transmissibility of acquired characters.

But the confessed failure so far of biologists to clear up the process of evolution, or
experimentally to create a new species from
an existing one, does not affect the facts derived from many converging sources which
lead to the unavoidable conclusion that man

has a genealogical relation to the higher animals.

It is the discovery of man's animal extraction, rather than evolution in general, that troubles those who do not stop to consider the matter carefully. Many are willing to admit that it looks as if life had developed on the earth slowly, in successive stages; this they can regard as a merely curious fact and of no great moment if only man can be defended as an honorable exception. The fact that we have an animal body may also be conceded, but surely, it is urged, man must have a soul and a mind altogether distinctive and unique from the very beginning, setting him off an immeasurable distance from any mere animal.

And so he has! It is precisely the evolutionary hypothesis that makes it possible to realize to the full the absolute uniqueness of man and his boundless possibilities. He seems to have sprung from the lower animals, but that makes his *manhood* all the more impressive. He can only hope to appreciate it and illuminate it in the light of his origin and affinities. He can, in short, for the first time see what he is by recognizing what he was in the beginning.

So we should not be repelled and humiliated by the evidence that man's *mind* is quite as clearly of animal extraction as his *body*. Those older observations classed under paleontology, zoology, comparative anatomy, biochemistry, physiology and embryology, which reveal innumerable likenesses and affinities between man and the higher mammals in structure, function and development from the egg, are now being paralleled by observations, classed under comparative psychology, functional psychology, anthropology, prehistoric archeology and intellectual history, which show that man's mind like his body is akin in its original nature and fundamental operations to that of the higher animals.

The historical and comparative methods of approaching the study of the human body are largely responsible for our present rapidly growing understanding of it. The historical and comparative study of psychological phenomena—of what we call reasoning, emotions, impulses, the will—promise to be quite as clarifying and revolutionary when it can

be freely applied. It will alter the whole conception of the various old divisions of philosophy and tend to put these hitherto rather unreal and half mythical subjects on a firmer foundation of observable facts. To cite a single example of this hopeful tendency; John Dewey has recently written a book called "Human Nature and Conduct" in which he frankly reverses the usual procedure of writers on ethics. He first takes up the habits and workings of the human being and then attempts to deduce the general rules that would seem appropriate to a creature like man. Now, the moralists in the past have in general neglected just these things, of which with their mistaken presuppositions they could at best know but little, and have devoted their attention to accepted standards of conduct, ancient and dubious in origin, which they sought to justify by subtle theories and ingenious applications. This was, of course, to do little more than to defend and perpetuate, rather than to revise and readjust, the prevailing morals and *mores*: hence the general barrenness of ethics as commonly understood.

Those who follow the recent development in philosophy can not fail to see how deeply it is influenced by the methods and discoveries of natural science. Indeed this old distinction between "natural" science and our knowledge of man himself is an artificial and misleading one. Man is an integral part of the natural order; he and his environment are constantly interacting. Such well-tried old terms as the will, consciousness, selfishness, the instincts, etc., when reinspected in the light of our ancestral background and embryological beginnings, all look very different from what they once did.

The soul is no longer the pale little creature, *Hospes comesque corporis,* as described in Emperor Hadrian's famous lines. Nor is the human body—made up, as it now appears to be, exclusively of electrical charges—so lumpish a thing as once it seemed. Mind and matter can no longer be divorced but must be studied as different phases of a single vital and incredibly complicated situation. Mind is still in the making. And a historical consideration of human intelligence, taking into account its animal and prehistoric foundations, its development in historic times, and the decisive childhood experiences through which each of us individually must pass—all these combine to reveal previously neglected elements in our minds and untold possibilities in their future growth.

V: On Science *vs* Lore, and the Current Hostility to a Scientific Attitude of Mind

V: On Science *vs* Lore, and the Current Hostility to a Scientific Attitude of Mind

Science, we ought always to recollect, is nothing more or less than the most accurate and best authenticated information that exists, subject to constant rectification and amplification, of man and his world. It is by no means confined to stars, chemicals, physical forces, rocks, plants and animals, as is often assumed. There is a scientific way of looking at ourselves—our thoughts, feelings, habits and customs; at their origin and interworkings. *Science, in short, includes all the careful and critical knowledge we have about anything of which we can come to know something.*

Perhaps the easiest way of getting a notion of the unity and comprehensiveness of science is to set it off against *lore*[1] of various kinds—traditional beliefs which recommend them-

---

[1] This is one of Veblen's ironical words. See his admirable *Place of Science in Modern Civilization*, essays I and II.

selves in virtue of their familiarity, antiquity, sanctity, nobility, goodness or general acceptance by respectable people. These beliefs seems to many firm and lasting compared with the ever shifting and tentative conclusions reached through scientific research and reexamination. A great part of mankind is taught to believe that ancient prophets and seers were wiser than we can hope to be, and that divine truth was vouchsafed them which can never be transcended, and should never be questioned by the scientifically disposed. Those who oppose Faith to Reason do not think of Faith as blind, but as divinely keen-eyed and secure, as well as sweet and comforting. All mystics are at one in this. Scientific investigation, they would concede, has its own sphere, but it is limited by God's word, as they have been taught to interpret it, and by the narrow compass of the human understanding.

We are all familiar with this attitude toward revealed and mystic truth, and it has long been a subject of bitter controversy whether the Bible should be read and studied and criticized like any other collection of ancient writings, and its contents interpreted in the light of the beliefs and the ignorances prevailing at the time its various parts were written or revealed. Comparatively few persons even yet have any scientific knowledge of the Bible, such as is easily available in such delightful books as Solomon Reinach's *Orpheus,* George F. Moore's *Literature of the Old Testament,* Morris Jastrow's *Gentle Cynic;* Conybeare's *Myth, Magic and Morals.* Accordingly one of the great obstacles to a spread of scientific thought is still the old conception of the Bible.

Our childhood impressions are likely to be permanent unless circumstances are very favorable for their later modification. We would tend to become scientifically minded the moment we began to suspect that the people with whom we associated in childhood were in all probability hardly abreast of the times, as the saying is. We might conjecture that much had probably been found out about both evolution and the Bible during the last half century which had escaped us. And our suspicions, could they be aroused, would probably be amply justified.

The same confidence in *lore* as contrasted with science may be noted not merely in religious beliefs but in traditional ideas of morality, patriotism, private property, the state, the family, war, etc. To cite a single example: One who pronounces birth control sinful, opposed to religion and sound morality and who contends that the dissemination of knowledge in regard to contraceptual methods is "obscene," takes a stand and uses a vocabulary approved by moral tradition.

On the other hand one might see in the issue a curious and essential problem. Without being driven to prompt and final condemnation he might feel free to think the matter over in the light of such knowledge as he might gain. He would first remedy his ignorance of human embryology and of the way in which each of us comes about. He would ponder on the hallowed methods of reducing births through monastic institutions and the enforced celibacy of the clergy, or by economic pressure. He might then turn to the larger questions of the relation of birth control to disease, mental deficiency, poverty and the question of over population. Then, and then only, might he be ready from a scientific standpoint to form some opinion on the probable expediency of repealing our present laws relating to this matter. No one would question the propriety of such an approach were it not assumed that there is something essentially improper in submitting the case to the verdict of intelligence.

Havelock Ellis wisely says: "It may seem that in setting forth the nature of the sexual impulse in the light of modern biology and psychology, I have said but little of purity and less of morality. Yet that is as it should be. We must first be content to see how the machine works and watch the wheels go round. We must understand before we can control."[1] And to understand requires pains and care. It will not do simply to shut our eyes and be sure that we are right. Of all human ambitions an open mind eagerly expectant of new discoveries and ready to remould convictions in the light of added knowledge and dispelled ignorances and misapprehensions, is the noblest, the rarest, and the most difficult to achieve.

---

[1] *Little Essays of Love and Virtue* (Doran) p. 55.

What is true of the general attitude toward religion and sex is true also of our prevailing notions of politics, business, international relations and education. There is much defensive and offensive discussion but no great play of intelligence. Even those who attack existing institutions, ideas and habits often do so in a semi-religious spirit. The good and the bad, right and wrong, just and unjust are apt to be the *starting point* rather than the *outcome* of the inquiry. And yet, if we but stop to think, all these seemingly so solid and reliable things have varied tremendously in different times and places. We have to find out what things are good and right and just, before we can appropriate them. They are not labelled, ready to our hand.

And yet they are tacitly assumed to be settled, at least in their larger aspects. It is not supposed to be well or safe to invite the young or the "masses" to think of important matters with a critically open mind. The traditional lore must first be instilled and then only, if at all, may some thoughtfulness be permitted. But it is usually agreed that this should be controlled and, directed by those wise and prudent persons who are keenly alive to the dangers of doubt and skepticism and who are sure to come out just where they went in. I take it this is the attitude of the overwhelming majority of good and respectable people, who in the last analysis control our education and represent the taste to which newspapers, magazines and lecturers must appeal. There is, in short, some confidence in the value of scientific discussion within certain limits, but so far as man and his doings are concerned it is as yet far from sanctioned by public opinion.

No one can be more poignantly conscious of the groping nature of intelligence than I. The misgivings of the mystics as to our ability to reach ultimate truth are shared by every scientifically-minded person. If we could be assured that there exist better, more secure and more profound sources of knowledge than human intelligence we ought, of course, to accept them. But as yet the human mind can hardly be said to have had a show, and I, for one, have faith that if we gave it a show, mere human intelligence, based upon our ever increasing knowledge, would tend to remedy or greatly alleviate many forms of human discontent and misery. This is a matter of faith, I admit. But holding this faith, the chief end of education seems to me to be the encouragement of a scientific attitude of mind and a full and vivid appreciation of the inherent obstacles that oppose themselves to its successful cultivation in the human species.

Fifty years ago Matthew Arnold described the aim of education as "The getting to know on all matters which concern us the best which has been thought and said in the world; and through this knowledge turning a stream of fresh and free thought upon our stock notions and habits." He also said that we do not change our minds as the result of logic and refutation; but as we learn more the ground gently shifts beneath us, and we no longer look at things as we formerly did. This is so very true and so very important! I am sure that attempts directly to cultivate the judgment through teaching logic or the various branches of science have failed and are destined always to fail. At bottom they are an unconscious avoidance of the responsibility which would be involved in really turning a stream of fresh and free thought upon our stock notions and habits. *We are not yet in a position so to revise our education that a new type of mind will be cultivated appropriate to our present knowledge and circumstances.*

For education is controlled to a large extent by those who still adhere to many ancient conceptions which appear to them to be based on the best wisdom of the past, to be tested by time and substantiated by a consensus of human experience. These they do not wish to see disturbed. No two persons might agree as to exactly what these approved findings are, but so long as a notion is familiar it is assumed that it will not do any particular harm.

Now, new knowledge, if taken seriously, is very likely to prove an indictment of those very ideas which are dearest to the ill-informed. So in order to avoid inconvenient discussion the doctrine has become popular that so-called "controversial" matters should be carefully excluded from both the schools and colleges.

This means, when stated in a bald form,

that instruction which might stir religious distrust, no matter how unintelligent, business, political or racial prejudice, or violate the proprieties, must be avoided. College presidents, school superintendents, text-book writers and their publishers are at present almost helpless in this situation. Teaching must be made as little disturbing as possible, when its chief function should be to stimulate thought and furnish new and reconstructive ideas.

The plight of the directors of education is indeed pitiable. College presidents have to sit up late at night reconciling the noble doctrine of freedom of teaching with the practical necessity of dodging controversial questions—for at all costs nothing must happen to arouse the resentment of timid parents and donors. The college head can not endure the humiliating imputation that his teachers are under "the wardship of an overweening fist," as Milton puts it; and yet he is constantly haunted by the nightmare of the fist which will refuse to write any more checks to the order of the institution if an instructor is carelessly charged by some ill-informed onlooker with "Bolshevism," "radicalism," or "socialistic leanings."

For what is perhaps still worse, the religious, moral or patriotic critics rarely take the trouble to find out what an instructor or text-book writer whom they attack really has said or believes. This scandalous state of affairs is too little understood. Those best informed about it are for various reasons disinclined to tell all they know. Those who plan out courses of study and write books for the schools are not free, but must often make very humiliating terms with unintelligence.

Matthew Arnold's ideal would be accepted in theory by most educators, but how very far are we from realizing it in practice. Teachers and text-book writers can not proceed directly toward this goal as they conceive it. They must hedge and suppress, compromise and extenuate, lest the authentic facts which it concerns boys and girls to learn should unluckily start them thinking.[1] For this might rouse the apprehension of some defender of the social and moral order, some professional patriot or some adherent of the Mosaic authorship of the Pentateuch. The politicians in the Kentucky and other legislatures think themselves competent to decide whether the state should grant funds to any institution in which man's animal extraction is taught; the politicians in the New York legislature provided that no one should teach in the schools of the state who was known at any time to have expressed any distrust of our institutions.[1]

Now nothing could be more diametrically opposed to the cultivation of a scientific frame of mind. Education ought to be largely devoted to the issues upon which the young as they grow up should be in a position to form

---

[1] In reviewing my *Mind in the Making* Professor Harry N. Gardiner of Smith College says: The book is full, as it seems to him, of "crudities and exaggerations." "When for example, it is asserted (p. 11) that no publisher would accept a historical text-book based on an explicit statement of our present knowledge of man's animal ancestry, it is hard to believe that we are dealing with a statement of fact and not rather an opinion expressing a prejudiced animus" (*American Historical Review*, Vol. xxvi, p. 768, July, 1922). I fear that one of the difficulties in the way of educational reform is that of convincing such worthy persons as Professor Gardiner that what I am saying here is not merely the delusions of one afflicted with a persecution complex. Having been writing and editing historical text books for a quarter of a century I can only invite Professor Gardiner to consult the text-book publishers as to the truth of the facts given above.

an intelligent opinion. They should understand that scientific advance has greatly altered, and promises still further to alter, our
environment and our notions of ourselves and
possibly the expediency of existing moral,
social and industrial standards.

We should have a dynamic education to fit
a dynamic world. The world should not be
presented to students as happily standardized
but as urgently demanding readjustment.
How are they to be more intelligent than
their predecessors if they are trained to an
utterly unscientific confidence in ancient notions, let us say of religion, race, heredity and
sex, now being so fundamentally revised.[1]

---

[1] One who wishes to study this matter is referred to Veblen,
The Higher Learning in America, a profound analysis of the
deep-lying deficiencies of our system, full of somewhat esoteric
humor: Upton Sinclair, *The Goose-step,* in which a wealth
of material is collected which will startle and perhaps vex
those who have never considered the half-unconscious coa-
lescence of forces directed against the full modernization of
our education. Some statements and some inferences in this
book appear to me hazardous, and I wonder if Mr. Sinclair
does not occasionally discover subtle demons of economic
greed where there are only panicky and ignorant college
presidents and trustees. See also Ludwig Lewisohn, *Up Stream*
and Samuel Butler's marvellous satire on higher education in
Erewhon, chaps. xxi-xxii. For the larger setting see Chaffee,
Freedom of Speech and Lippmann, *Public Opinion.*

VI: The Problem of Humanizing Knowledge

Elle était toute petite, ma vie; mais c'était une vie, c'est-à-dire le centre des choses, le milieu du monde.

ANATOLE FRANCE.

VI: The Problem of Humanizing Knowledge

Supposing it be conceded that one[1] at least of the objects of a general education is to help the young to become acquainted with the best that is now known or guessed about mankind and the world; that it concerns them to know this, and that it should be so presented that it will, by encouraging them to scrutinize our stock notions and habits, best prepare them to lead more intelligent lives and deal more wisely than their predecessors with old and new problems. How is progress in this direction to be made in view of the tremendous obstacles which have been briefly indicated in the preceding pages? How are mankind's guides and instructors to modernize their outlook in such a way as to free scientific intelligence from the suspicions which still beset

---

[1] I say *"one* at least of the objects" since we might aspire in addition to cultivate artistic taste and literary interest and discrimination or, as is very common, aim at specific preparation for a particular vocation or profession.

it and assure it the influence to which it is entitled? *This is the supreme problem of our age and no one can hope to do more than to make modest contributions to its solution.*

We have seen that modern scientific advance is due to what we have called its *dehumanization.* Those who carry on research seem oblivious in their work to the ordinary human craving for usefulness or beauty or spiritual exaltation. They devote themselves to minute and detailed study, for the successful prosecution of which years of application are necessary. So neither the methods nor the technical results of scientific research are likely to make a fundamental appeal to any except the professional researcher. And yet, as has been shown, the esoteric operations of the laboratory and study are literally re-creating man and his world. So just as once it was essential to *dehumanize* knowledge, now it must be *rehumanized.*

In order to accomplish this, or at least to advance toward its accomplishment, our knowledge of man and his world must be re-ordered and restated; it must be put together anew with full regard to the ways in which the average person assimilates new knowledge. It must be *resynthesized*. At present vital knowledge is torn up into fragments; shuffled into large piles labelled history, philosophy, psychology, philology, anthropology, ethics, politics, economics, astronomy, physics, chemistry, biology, geology, geography, botany. And each of these is divided into smaller piles—stellar physics, bio-chemistry, embryology, thermo-dynamics, optical mineralogy, prehistoric archaeology, epistemology, Latin epigraphy. But even these are too cumbersome and distracting and miscellaneous for the real specialist, who finds his life work in classifying the white corpuscles of the human body, in the oscillations of the electrons, or German music before Luther.

All these are instances of the historical division of labor; they have a certain appropriateness for the researcher but are being constantly transgressed as investigators become more fully aware of the essential interweaving and interdependence of all things. Dr. Spoehr, of the Carnegie laboratory at Carmel, has remarked that the study of photosynthesis—the process by which the living chlorophyl cells of plants utilize sunlight to produce essential chemical changes—had been kept back a hundred years because it got side-tracked by happening to be classified under "plant physiology." If one looks over the program of a meeting of anatomists they seem nowadays to be engaged in investigations which have little to do with what most of us have been taught to regard as anatomy.

These divisions of knowledge, great and small, have a significance in research, but they form one of the most effective barriers to the cultivation of a really scientific frame of mind in the young and the public at large. In the enterprise of rehumanizing knowledge it is necessary first to recognize that specialization, so essential in research, is putting us on the wrong track in education. This has been suspected for some time; nevertheless even the latest scheme of educational reform which reaches me proposes that we continue to classify our instruction under social sciences, natural sciences and language—to which some might be tempted to add, the fine arts.

Representatives of these branches are summoned to testify as to the significance and setting that should be assigned to their particular sciences in a new attempt "to enable our youth to realize what it means to live in society, to appreciate how people have lived and do live together, and to understand the conditions essential to living together well; to the end that our youth may develop such abilities, inclinations and ideals as may qualify them to take an intelligent and effective part in an evolving society."[1] This is surely the great aim of modern education, excellently expressed; but I wonder why we should think of history, economics, politics and geography as distinctively social sciences; language is pretty social too; and why is geography more social than chemistry or physics or botany? The importance of all of them lies in their relation to ourselves and our fellow men.

As Dr. Charles Beard has said: "Every field of human knowledge is so vast that the workers therein are driven, in their endeavour to see things as they really are, further

---

[1] Preliminary report of the Joint Commission on the "Purpose of Social Studies in Our Schools." This committee represents several associations devoted to the various social sciences.

and further into details of their subject. They then easily forget the profound truth enunciated by Buckle that the science of any subject is not at its centre but at its periphery where it impinges upon all other sciences. So the living organism of human society as a subject of inquiry has been torn apart and parcelled out among specialists."[1]

Professor Frederick Soddy, the well-known British physicist, recently began a lecture before the London School of Economics with the words[2]: "It is my intention to try to bring the existing knowledge of the physical sciences to bear upon the question 'How do men live?' This question ought to be the first the economist should try to answer . . . but the modern economist seems to have forgotten that there is such a question, whilst the earlier ones lived at a stage of the development of scientific knowledge when no exact answer was forthcoming. . . . In the present state of science, the answer to the question how men live, or how anything lives

---

[1] *The Economic Basis of Politics*, 1922, pp. 14-15.

[2] *Cartesian Economics, The Bearing of Physical Science upon State Stewardship*, by Frederick Soddy, London, 1922, p. 32.

. . . is, with few and unimportant exceptions, 'By sunshine.'" Certainly, Professor Soddy is quite right; one might expect to run up against sunshine in a treatise on astronomy, chemistry, physics or plant physiology, but hardly in an economic handbook. Yet he manages by beginning with sunshine to show how much of our so-called science of wealth is inept, and how true is Professor Leacock's definition of Political Economy as that science "which teaches that we know nothing of the laws of wealth." And we surely shall never know about wealth if sunshine is left out. For the sun is the ultimate wealth producer, giving us life and food and light and power and raw materials, none of which either capital or labor, or both combined, can furnish, bitterly as they may struggle over and waste the solar revenue.

One of our foremost biologists expresses his astonishment that, when the general story of man's knowledge of nature has been so frequently and so clearly explained, there are still men of letters like G. K. Chesterton who declares that science is "a thing on the outskirts of human life," that "it has nothing to

do with the center of human life at all."
This is bad enough, but he reports his further consternation when one of his biological
confrères boasted that when besieged by soci-
ologists, economists and educators who de-
sired to learn what biology had to do with
their problems, replied "Biology has nothing
to say about such matters." He reflects that
biology takes endless pains to understand
the behavior of sea anemones, earth worms,
crabs, frogs, crows, mice, but makes official
declaration that with the behavior of one
species of animal, namely man, it is practically unconcerned.[1]

It would seem from this evidence that there
is a failure not only on the part of the busy
mass of mankind but on the part of men of
letters, economists and even scientists themselves to appreciate the tremendous import
of our accumulations of knowledge. The
scholarly and learned have to be converted as
well as the "fundamentalists" and other static
or reactionary groups. We are all shamefully
uneducated, whether we be learned in some

---

[1] *The Higher Usefulness of Science* by William Emerson
Ritter, pp. 54-55.

particular field or not; and this lack of scientific insight is naturally more striking in those that dedicate themselves to intellectual interests than in the average citizen, absorbed in assuring himself and his family a livelihood.

Those who devote their professional lives to literature can probably look back to the vain efforts of their awkward teachers of science to adorn them with a dab or two from Science's iris-hued brush and their lasting resentment at the attempt to discolor their poetic or romantic souls. In later life they compensate themselves for their gross ignorance of natural processes by declaring, as Mr. Chesterton does, that science is irrelevant to our deeper lives; or as Brunetière did, that science is bankrupt.

As for the economist he is the victim of unfortunate traditions in his analysis of human wealth, its production and distribution. He, too, is likely to have gained only lifeless notions of natural science and sees no way of weaving them into his scheme of things. He, moreover, almost inevitably finds himself, perhaps unconsciously, assuming that the particular business practices of his generation are a reflection of "economic laws."

Finally men of science themselves have a wholly inadequate setting for their specialized research. They rightly suspect that the social sciences are not sciences in their sense of the term. They know how very hard it is to get any exact knowledge about anything. Immersion in their particular researches, lack of time for other things, and an honorable diffidence keep most of them, like the exemplary shoemaker, at their last.

In any case there can be no doubt that many things still interfere with the proper interplay between the so-called natural and social sciences; and each of these grand divisions of human knowledge, which belong so intimately together, dealing as they do with man and his world, are artificially separated by old boundary lines, defended against invaders and smugglers by jealous vested interests. *This is the inevitable outcome of transplanting into our educational system the technical divisions of scientific research.*

Our various scientific courses rarely produce either of the main results to be expected from them. They neither engender in the student a discriminating and exacting tendency of mind—that combination of open-mindedness and caution which should be the finest fruit of successful scientific training; nor do they foster such a lively understanding of the workings of nature that the fascination of discovering ever new wonders will endure through life and mitigate sorrow, boredom and disappointment. Of course, judged by this standard, the failure of education is no less conspicuous in the fields of literature, history, language and philosophy.

The problem has apparently two phases. One, how is human knowledge to be so ordered and presented in school and college as to produce permanent effects and an attitude of mind appropriate to our time and its perplexities: the other, how is knowledge to be popularized and spread abroad among adults who have become dissatisfied with what they know and are eager to learn more. Since, however, there is no great difference in the ways in which the overwhelming majority of young and old really learn, these two phases need not be discussed separately. Both the text books and manuals used in formal teaching and the various popular presentations of scientific facts written for adults tend, almost without exception, to classify knowledge under the generally accepted headings mentioned above. They have a specious logic and orderliness which appeals to the academic mind. They, therefore, suit the teachers fairly well, but unhappily do not inspire the learners.

When one has gone through a text book and safely weathered the examination he rarely has any further use for it. This is not because he has really absorbed it and so need not refer to it again. On the contrary, it is associated with a process alien to his deeper and more permanent interests. And it is being found by those who embark in adult education that text books make almost no appeal to grown-ups, who are free to express their distaste for them.

Teaching is one thing, learning, as we are slowly coming to see, quite another. Teaching aims to be logical; learning is strangely illogical, or rather, has its own logic and its own effective methods which have hitherto been almost completely disregarded. The "principles" or "elements" of a branch of science are really the ultimate outcome of a knowledge of it, not the thin edge of the wedge which insinuates it into our minds.

Let anyone review what he has learned in life. He will find that his effective and living knowledge has come in the most informal and seemingly casual manner. It has crystalized about unexpected nuclei. Chance happenings have aroused interest, and interest has bred curiosity, and curiosity has begotten learning. Most of what passes for learning is a kind of pitiful affectation. The student says, "I have had" Latin or chemistry, or "I took" science or literature. All is safely in the past or the perfect tense, as if it were an attack of pleurisy or a boil.

On the other hand when one of Mr. Wells' hundreds of thousands of readers has finished his *Outline of History* he does not say, "I have *had* history" and—in his heart—"I hope never to have it again." And why? Because Mr. Wells manages to *humanize* the past of mankind. He may make mistakes, from the standpoint of the special student; he may make rash conjectures and display personal preferences in commenting on Caesar or Napoleon, but people who had never realized the general way in which man came about, or how writing originated; had never thought of Gautama, the Buddha, or the origin of the Bible, feel, as they read, something really happening in them, and with the new knowledge things never seem to them again as they seemed before. This constitutes learning. The history teacher often suspects that the students are by no means honestly convinced that any of the people mentioned in the text book ever lived, that the council of Nicaea ever occurred, or Lady Jane Grey's girlish little head was ever cut off.

Let us take another illustration. There are certain very important considerations about men and women and love which it concerns human beings to know. Havelock Ellis, after years of scientific investigation of sexual phenomena, embodied in a series of volumes, has lately written his *Little Essays of Love and Virtue*. It fits into no recognized scientific category; into no standardized department of instruction, for his aim is to really modify existing standards and permanently alter the ideas, aspirations and conduct of young people. He says "I would prefer to leave to their judgment the question as to whether this book is suitable to be placed in the hands of older people. It might only give them pain." He perceives one of the implications of humanizing important knowledge. Too often the old can't stand it.

The best presentation of the basis and implications of psychanalysis which I have met is embodied in a recent novel by Elsa Barker.[1] Few can read the book without being deeply and permanently influenced by it even if they were already somewhat familiar with the numerous systematic treatises in this field. She has humanized the subject by bringing it within our own experiences.

Other books might be mentioned which boldly disregard the traditional classification of knowledge, and were they only simplified would meet the needs of great numbers of readers, both old and young. Of such I may mention Dewey's *Human Nature and Conduct,* John A. Hobson's *Democracy after the*

---

[1] *Fielding Sargent* (Dutton).

War, Mumford's *The Story of Utopia,* Beard's *Cross Currents in Europe,* Tawney's *Acquisitive Society,* Wallas's *Social Heritage,* Bertrand Russell's *Why Men Fight,* Charles S. Myers' *Mind and Work*—these and many others represent promising new and pertinent syntheses, but some of them are not sufficiently free from a certain academic staidness which stands in the way of their wide diffusion.

I am inclined to guess that it would make little difference to the readers of these books whether or not they had had formal instruction in the various fields of knowledge from which the writers have drawn. Personally I have reached the conclusion, after many years of teaching, that one should choose for instruction, whether one be dealing with young or old, *some phase of human interest rather than some field of scientific investigation,* select the book that treats it best and then bring to bear all the available knowledge by way of criticism or elaboration that may be found ordered up in the systematic manuals.

But most of the best books are simply too long and too hard for even ambitious and intelligent readers. For to be simple is to be sympathetic and to endeavor to bring what one says or writes close up to those one is addressing. We are not many of us interested in isolated scientific facts of any kind. That species of interest, as we have seen, is reserved for the few. But all of us are open to the effects of such new knowledge as gets under our skin. And the great art in writing is not to exhibit one's own insight and learning but really to influence those whom one is aiming to influence.

History is a field where all sorts of new patterns can be made, for it is nothing more or less than all our information about the past. I have spent a good many years selecting the evidence that bears on the development and fortunes of what for a better name I called the "Intellectual class." In forming this new synthesis I found myself a trespasser roaming about in the preserves of the philosopher, theologian, anthropologist, comparative psychologist, prehistoric archelogist and of the historians both of literature and science—to mention only a few of my encroachments. Now this has proved very amusing and instructive to me, and I have found many hundreds of young men and women to follow me in my wanderings.

When we got through we had discovered a new world, and man's past and the possibilities of his future were no longer what we had taken them to be. What I have done others can do in better and more ingenious ways; and the history of man's achievements and growing understanding of himself and his world could be made a branch of study beginning early and running through all the years of school and college. For, as Francis Bacon said, the history of the world without the story of man's education is like a figure of the mighty giant Polyphemus with his single great eye left out.

We need, therefore, a new class of writers and teachers, of which there are already some examples, who are fully aware of what has been said here and who see that the dissipation of knowledge should be offset by an integration, novel and ingenious, and necessarily tentative and provisional. They should undertake the conscious adventure of humanizing knowledge. There are minds of the requisite temper, training and literary tact. They must be hunted out, encouraged and brought together in an effective if informal conspiracy to promote the diffusion of the best knowledge we have of man and his world. They should have been researchers at some period of their lives, and should continue to be researchers in another sense. Their efforts would no longer be confined to increasing knowledge in detail but in seeking to discover new patterns of what is already known or in the way to get known.

They should be re-assorters, selecters, combiners and illuminators. They should have a passion for diffusing, by divesting knowledge as far as possible of its abstract and professional character. At present there is a woeful ignorance even among persons who pass for intelligent, earnest and well read, in regard to highly important matters that are perfectly susceptible of clear general statement.

The reassorters and humanizers should combine a knowledge of the exigencies of scientific research with a philosophic outlook, human sympathy, and a species of missionary ardor. Each of them should have professional familiarity with some special field of knowledge, but this should have come to seem to him but a subordinate feature of the magnificent scientific landscape.

A good deal of courage is necessary too. Some of us experience a certain sense of outlawry when we wander beyond the assured precincts of our guild. This will amuse or depress us according to our mood. As Mrs. Mary Austin remarks: "What determines the rank of the science researcher is the uncolored virginity of his approach, free even from sympathy with his own hypothesis, ruthless toward any attempt to implicate his findings with their effect on a possible bystander. The moment he takes the bystander into account, or attempts to interpret discovery in terms of the average mind, he must abandon this fine inviolateness and shift his facts so that they are patterned around the lacunae in the minds of his audience rather than by their intrinsic relation to discoverable truth. The scientist who does this once, successfully, will not be able to resist the temptation to do it again, and after a third time it will be left for his brother scientists to remark that the chilled edge of his mind never comes back to him."

Mrs. Austin further observes, truly enough, that: "Literature is produced not by taking pains but by having them. The whole sum of objective material must pass in and out of the writer's consciousness and be chemically combined there until, touching the consciousness of the reader, it explodes and fires the mind. Without this explosion there is no alteration of the thought pattern, and reading science becomes a pastime about as invigorating as playing solitaire. . . . Science must in its own behalf deduce out of the common psychology a method of producing the necessary explosion in the reader's mind without distortion."[1]

There is a rapidly .increasing and altogether encouraging discontent with schools and colleges, which shows itself even among the hitherto docile student bodies. It is becoming evident that the main trouble does not lie in the unimaginative and sometimes

[1] "Science for the Unscientific," *The Bookman,* August, 1922, Vol. lv, No. 6.

tyrannical form of administration; nor is it to be met by devising new ways of teaching old "subjects" or by adding new ones. We must look to the very core of what is getting learned and ask whether this is producing a frame of mind befitting our times. It would seem that we have been extraordinarily indifferent in regard to precisely this all-essential consideration.

The object of this little volume is the attempt to re-assess our failures and possibilities in the development of intelligence; especially to make clear why, proceeding as we have done, we have inevitably failed to make connection between education on the one hand and the obligations, pit falls and amenities of life on the other. The whole substance and aims and methods of education—whether for young or old—need a thorough overhauling and reconsideration. Something should be devised to replace the old liberal arts courses. A good idea underlay it, but its alleged results will no longer stand inspection in the light of modern knowledge and modern conditions of life. The elective system also has a good idea behind it, namely a recognition of the student's spontaneous interests and preferences. But it also is a confession that the tree of knowledge has of late put forth so many and such thick branches that the main trunk is lost sight of. The stately proportions of science are obscured by its details.

At present going through college rarely makes any decisive change in the mood and outlook of the graduate. There is, it is true, the old saying that you can always tell a Harvard man, but you can't tell him much. But like most caustic remarks it does not hit the mark. The college graduate is no longer arrogant but timid and bewildered when he discovers himself in a strange world for which he has been so expensively unprepared. He ordinarily prizes his experience in college in retrospect for various adventitious friendlinesses rather than for a fuller understanding of himself and his surroundings.

What we need most, as I have tried to make plain, is a new intellectual mood, a new tolerance of intelligent divergence of opinion, a new appreciation of the rôle of knowledge in human planning. In order to achieve this we can well afford to be more courageous and adventurous than our predecessors in view of the infinite possibilities of further enlightenment that have opened before us. Our knowledge must be recast so as to become a part of our daily reckonings. And many are the ways in which this can be done. Our efforts in this direction will necessarily be groping and provisional at first, and subject to constant revision, as conditions change and knowledge grows. And when recast, it must be humanized, so as to make it slip into our train of thought, and progress there under its own power. If authentic knowledge could in some way be identified with the experiences of the child and youth, a deeper import would no longer lurk in the legends told us in our infant years than in "the truth we live to learn."[1]

---

[1] Remy de Gourmont likens education to a bag of salt, laboriously loaded onto a donkey's back, and sure to melt in the first storm. The object of education is, of course, permanently to improve the creature, not to impose an evanescent load on him. But the task is a hard one and the difficulties offered by the animal's nature and preferences can not be overcome either by coercion or by trying to forget them.

VII: How is Scientific Knowledge to be Democratized?

VII: How is Scientific Knowledge to be Democratized?

It is far easier to make general reflections upon human problems than to devise and carry out measures for solving them. We are most of us ready enough to suspect that things are not all they should be, but suggestions of possible ways to better them are apt to be dismissed as too laborious, inadequate or troublesome. Growling is congenial in certain moods, but these are just the moods in which the prospect of painful effort is most distasteful. Those professionally engaged in the business of education are wont, as Veblen puts it, to indulge themselves in "truculent quietism." This permits a free expression of discontent without threatening comfortable habits. And the hazards and inconveniencies of changing habits are commonly far more impressive than the dangers of adhering to them. It is therefore with considerable diffidence that the writer takes the risk of adding a few rather more specific criticisms and suggestions.

There are, and have long been, many attempts to popularize knowledge. Our schools and colleges are ostensibly devoted to this; and there are many books, articles and lectures directed to the same end. The results, however, seem very inadequate compared with the possibilities. Some of the reasons for our past failures have been pointed out. It has become apparent that we must fundamentally reorder and readjust our knowledge before we can hope to get it into the current of our daily thought and conduct. It must be re-synthesized and re-humanized. It must be made to seem vitally relevant to our lives and deeper interests.

But even if this arduous task were accomplished, requiring as it does great courage, ingenuity and patience, still another awaits us if our constantly increasing scientific knowledge is to reach the multitudes. Our methods of presentation must be altered to meet new needs, and the habits of publishers must be modified in order to have a prospect of affecting millions of people.

At present so-called "serious" books, even when they pretend to be of a popular nature, are rarely written exclusively for the general reader. Scholars and men of science almost always write more or less unconsciously for one another. This is a natural outcome of their training. They must prove their preparation to deal with the subject in hand. They cannot forget their fellow workers in the field, and properly wish to enjoy the reputation of scientists and scholars and not that of mere popularizers. They are so accustomed to technical terms that they use them without realizing how few of their readers can be expected to understand them. This is the result not of a love of pedantic display but an acceptance of the rules of the game as they have been taught it.

They fear criticism on the part of members of their learned guild. The specter haunts them, not of a puzzled and frustrated reader, but of a tart reviewer, likely to accuse them of superficiality or inaccuracy. There is a heavy prejudice in learned circles against the popularizer. Those who are disinclined, or mayhap unable, to write plainly and pleasantly for the layman, are prone to denounce all attempts to popularize knowledge as vain or as mere expedients to keep the pot boiling.

Scientifically and philosophically trained writers apparently have no idea how hard their books and articles are for the general reader; how much is included that few can appreciate; how many statements are dark and unintelligible to those for whom the book is ostensibly designed. An encyclopædia or dictionary would seem to be compiled especially for the benefit of the public who are urged to buy it. But the seeker for knowledge who happens to have his curiosity aroused in regard to the polarization of light will find the article in the Encyclopædia Britannica beginning: "A stream of light coming directly from a natural source has no relation to space except that concerned in its direction of propagation, round which its properties are alike on all sides." Like the lovers in Dante's *Commedia,* the simple inquirer is likely to read no farther that day.

A seasoned teacher and a thinker of varied and penetrating insight ventures to begin an article relating to the humanizing of knowledge with the words: "It has become a commonplace of the psychologist that there is a structure in our experience which runs out beyond what we ordinarily term ·our consciousness; that this structure of idea determines to a degree not generally recognized the very manner of our perception as well as that of our thinking, and yet that structure itself is generally not in the focus of our attention and passes unnoticed in our thought and perceiving." This is a very revolutionary discovery and, if widely understood, might make the world look very different to the more alert and intelligent inhabitants of Auburn, Maine, or Billings, Montana; but there is grave danger of its continuing to pass unnoticed so long it is expressed in the form above.

These illustrations are not rare exceptions —they might easily be multiplied indefinitely. The style of our serious books is still under the influence of a tenacious scholastic tradition. It is very hard to escape from it sufficiently to meet the real demands of the public. We sadly need something between the half-academic phraseology used in most so-called popular works, and the other extreme of "journalese," with its condescending intimacy and jocosity.

We need, in short, a new form of literary ambition if scientific knowledge is to reach a fair proportion of the population and the scientific mood is to be widely cultivated. This ambition should be to bring home to the greatest possible number of readers as much knowledge as possible, in the most pleasing, effective, and least misleading manner. Few indeed there be who have this ambition, combined with the requisite knowledge, skill and sympathetic imagination to achieve it. Of all literary forms it is probably the most difficult and exacting.

A book or article for the general reader— a being, we may safely assume, with no great surplus of time, preparation, attention or initial interest—must do three things. And these three things it should do whether it be a sermonette by Dr. Crane in four or five hundred words, or a popular treatise on plant fertilization, the labor problem, or the history of architecture, running through four or five hundred pages. First, it should enlist the reader's attention. This must not be assumed, but must be wooed or conquered by graciousness or by force. There are many ways of doing this, but still more ways of failing. I suspect that success comes when the writer manages forthwith to identify the reader with the enterprise and make him feel that it concerns him personally and individually. In story writing it is of course recognized that the reader must be immediately captured, but scientific popularizers are prone to set a poor trap with no bait. The sense of obligation in the matter of serious reading seems to be somewhat on the ebb. It can no longer be relied upon in face of the varied competition offered by the modern novel and the magazines and newspapers.

The second duty of the writer is to present his facts and information in terms and in an order which will be understood by the reader and will fit into his ways of looking at things. Lastly, the significance of the information in its bearing on the reader's thought and conduct and his judgments of others should be wisely suggested. While none of these three requisites can be safely neglected if one hopes to attract and profit large numbers of readers, it is to be noted that in writing for scientists or scholarly fellow professors only the *second* requisite holds. It would indeed scarcely be courteous to assume that the professional reader's interest need be artificially stirred; and it would transcend the bounds of scientific decorum to hint that the facts given had any direct bearing on human life and conduct.

It is amusing to note the many things which college instructors and the writers of text books include in their lectures and manuals which they themselves would not be able to recollect between times. What a considerable and beneficent revolution would take place in teaching and writing if teacher and writer should confine himself, at least in addressing beginners or laymen, to telling only such facts as play so important a part in his own everyday thinking that he could recall them without looking them up! It is a good rule for a writer to assume that nothing in his favorite subject that fails to interest *him* vividly and persistently is likely to interest the outsider who reads his book. The specialist cannot, of course, expect others to be attracted by everything that has significance for him (for often meaning only comes with long application and much circumambient knowledge), and he certainly can hardly hope to impart effectively to others information which is barren to himself.

The story form is very congenial to the human mind, and the logic of a narrative or tale is always the best and surest form of appeal.   The narrowly logical presentation is almost sure to miss its aim.   Now that the historical and developmental approach has been discovered to be so fundamentally significant many essential observations in regard to man and his world can readily be cast into story form.   (Almost everything has come to seem a story to me!)

I appreciate too fully the tremendous difficulties of carrying out any such proposed scheme of simplification to think that it can be readily done at odd moments.   It will require special aptitude, strenuous application —*improbus labor,* as the poet puts it.   The scientist, philosopher and mathematician will urge that their speculations are simply out of range of the common man—and so they are in many instances. Yet it is conceivable that even the intelligent outsider might see what calculus was about; he is quite capable of understanding why wonder is aroused in regard to the fourth dimension and relativity; or why the specialist gets excited over colloids. It is perhaps not so very essential that he should have a general notion of these particular branches of knowledge and research— I have only cited them as the kind of things which are supposed to be hard to explain, even in a very general way, to a layman. It was Mill, I believe, who pointed out that a *general* idea is by no means necessarily a *superficial* idea. It may indeed be a very fundamental idea; and this scientists and philosophers seem to prefer to forget.

At present our books are not only too hard, they are also too long. I might mention a dozen excellent works published during the past year which may have sold in quantities ranging from two to three thousand copies. Had they been judiciously condensed to half or a third their length they might not only have been made twice or thrice as clear and effective, but might have reached tens of thousands of readers. But this wide availability and appeal could only have been achieved at the cost of much additional labor on the part of the writers. To produce *good, little* books, easy to slip into one's pocket or bag, would require a sort of red revolution among both authors and publishers. The sizes and weight of books, their paper and print, have their traditions like all else mortal.

As for magazine and newspaper articles, they often afford ingenious and promising examples of the humanizing of knowledge. But they are too short, unless the theme be a mere item or is treated in a very general fashion. They are ephemeral, easily mislaid, hard to dig out of their foreign setting. It is consequently, almost impossible to preserve them for future use. We are apt to read them hastily, as we do all periodical material, and then they are gone, leaving but a vague impression.

Moreover, those magazines which reach hundreds of thousands, not to say millions, of readers are largely supported by commercial advertising, which intrudes itself insolently into the so-called reading matter. The editors of such magazines have always to keep a weather-eye not only upon their subscription list but upon the main source of their revenue. They cannot allow any scientific information to reflect upon the interests and convictions of those who are by no means so absorbed in the democratization of scientific knowledge as they are in selling talc powder, soap, corsets, bathing suits, automobiles, or in the profits to be derived from some system of get-rich-quick psychology. Consequently, the editors of most popular magazines have a small herd of "sacred cows," so well bred as to be highly sensitive to any violation of the proprieties. Any impeachment of current business methods, any suspicion of immoral or irreligious tendencies, any indelicacy in stating natural processes, may offend their bovine susceptibilities, as every shrewd editor has learned to his cost.

I do not wish to exaggerate this element in the situation, but it is far more important than is commonly understood. It is surely unfortunate that as yet a great part of the inhabitants of the United States are getting all their notions of science and philosophy from under the suspicious noses of the sacred kine.

In spite of all that has been said, much improvement is certainly taking place, even with our present defective methods of disseminating scientific knowledge, and promoting a scientific attitude of mind. Progress is being made in many different ways, and new plans are being continually announced which promise to carry us nearer the goal. Writers will doubtless be found in increasing numbers who will be willing to spend twice the time on books half as large. And publishers may sometime recognize that the possibility of selling a hundred thousand copies at a dollar a copy may now and then outweigh the fair security of disposing of five thousand at three dollars and a half. All that has been urged in this essay is designed to encourage and stimulate these tendencies.

Is it not possible, however, that our book-making habits should be so far altered that we might have something between what now commonly passes for a book on the one hand and an article on the other? We do not need to be imprisoned between these two alternatives. A moderate-sized book contains from seventy-five thousand to a hundred and fifty thousand words; an article from three to five thousand. Publishing conditions are at present unfavorable to the writing and issuing of small volumes running from twenty to thirty or forty thousand words. And yet this should be the very range of sizes most appropriate for the carrying out of the suggestions made above.

The aim, it will be remembered, would not be to present the "outlines," or "elements," or "principles" of a whole recognized science, but to bring together our information on some rather specific theme sufficiently near and dear to a great many of us to have it excite and hold our attention so as to permit our previous notions and outlook to be permanently changed and broadened.

Books and articles are constantly appearing in which some happy contribution to the reordering and humanizing of knowledge is made. But such material would usually gain greatly by being reduced or expanded or simplified. The books are, as we have seen, too long and elaborate, the articles too short and ephemeral. When promising contributions are made by skilful and felicitous writers it would be possible, if there were any machinery for so doing, to arrange with the authors to readjust and adapt their material to fit into the plans here advocated.

A whole series of convenient and inexpensive little volumes might be issued—say six or eight yearly—in which new discoveries, and novel and promising ways of putting things together, could be embodied. For devices and inventions which relate to the putting together of facts should rank in importance with the discovery of the facts themselves. The topics need not be arranged in any particular order, for life and learning is scarcely an ordered thing, in any logical sense. The subjects might be as various as the interests of man. Each of us must, in the last analysis, make our own special synthesis of the knowledge and experience we acquire, which will continue to change as we live and learn.

The kind of topics I have in mind all have to do with the newer knowledge and guesses about man and his world. Every reader will immediately supply for himself topics about which his curiosity has been aroused. One might like to learn something of the theory of human conduct called "Behaviorism" or of the theory of knowledge called "Pragmatism." Another might wish to see what is meant by sunshine being the ultimate source of wealth. Another might have come to wonder whether, after all, it is money alone that "makes the mare go." The man who must read as he runs would be glad to have the whole notion of evolution sufficiently explained to understand that no well-informed person supposes that we are descended from monkeys. The discoveries relating to heredity, to youth and to old age, could be brought together in their bearing on the lives and fate of each and all of us. The confusion might be dissipated which identifies industrialism with the profit or price system. A more interesting little treatise could be written contrasting the ideals of ancient moralists and prophets with those of modern idealists, like Mr. H. G. Wells, who is deeply impressed with the undreamed-of possibilities opening before the human race. Indeed, the choice of topics is practically unlimited.

Those desirous of humanizing scientific knowledge will hardly attempt to lay siege directly to our institutions of learning. The academic traditions, timidities, routine and vested interests are all too well entrenched. But the new hopes of adult education offer an opening. This movement in England is the subject of a very important Parliamentary report, or "blue book," published by the Ministry of Reconstruction in 1919. Mr. Albert Mansbridge (founder of the Workers' Education Association of Great Britain and now chairman of the World Association for Adult Education) has been in this country encouraging similar ventures. Among other movements in this country for promoting adult education is the New School for Social Research, the Workers Education Bureau of America and many labor colleges and study circles. A series of promising volumes, called the "Workers' Bookshelf," is being planned and issued under the auspices of a committee of the Workers Education Bureau. Two of these volumes have already appeared.

The chief difficulty that adult education in all its forms encounters is the sad lack of really appropriate books of the kind we have been discussing. Adults have a strong, and in the main quite justifiable, dislike of text books. How, then, is the right kind of book to be supplied? Only by making those prepared to write such books conscious of the crying need for them.

But as things now stand neither the pursuit of science nor the occupancy of a chair in a university makes one scientifically minded in any broad sense—much less breeds any hopeful missionary ardor or social responsibility. Many researchers think the popularization of science either hopeless or needless. In their sense of the term it is probably both. But if no precautions are taken to bridge the gap between scientific knowledge and popular prejudice it may grow so wide that the researcher will find himself engulfed. A man of science has recently declared boldly and rightly that it is a scientific fact that "the emotional life of man *is primary.*" In the development of both the race and the individual "the human heart has the right of way. . . . Science must humbly reinstate itself as the instrument of humanity's desires. The needs of humanity render this no more imperative than does the perpetuation of science itself. And since intelligence does exist as the instrument of human need, intelligence must save its life by losing its pride."[1]

[1] "Bases of Bryanism," by Dr. T. V. Smith of the University of Chicago, *Scientific Monthly*, May, 1923, Vol. xvi, No. 5, p. 513.

PUBLISHER'S NOTE

The publishers of this book have pleasure in announcing that the plan outlined in the closing chapter by Dr. Robinson is in process of being worked out under his advice and with his personal help.

With the co-operation of the Workers Education Bureau, steps have been taken to secure the articles described by Dr. Robinson from a group of the ablest scientists in the United States and abroad. These will first be issued separately and later gathered together in a single volume to constitute an annual survey of the most important phases of human knowledge.

Details as to the first contributors and the date of publication of the proposed Year Book will be announced as soon as possible. Meanwhile, inquiries may be addressed either to Mr. Spencer Miller, Jr., Secretary of the Workers Education Bureau, 476 West 24th Street, New York City, or to George H. Doran Company, 244 Madison Avenue, New York City.